VA 0333 **987489** 8018

D1080251

Irish Poems

Matthew Sweeney was born in Co. Donegal, Ireland, in 1952. He lived in London for many years but has recently been spending time in Romania and Germany. He has published numerous books of poetry. His latest books are *Sanctuary*, *Selected Poems*, *Up on the Roof: Selected Poems for Children* and a children's novel, *Fox*.

Irish
Poems

Edited by Matthew Sweeney

MACMILLAN CHILDREN'S BOOKS

With thanks to the library of the Englisches Institut, Freie Universität of Berlin.

First published 2005
by Macmillan Children's Books
a division of Macmillan Publishers Ltd
20 New Wharf Road, London N1 9RR
Basingstoke and Oxford
www.panmacmillan.com

Associated companies throughout the world

ISBN 0 333 98748 9

3 5 7 9 8 6 4 2

Printed and bound in China

A CIP catalogue record for this book is available from the British Library.

Contents

Introduction

When I was first invited to put together for Macmillan a book of Irish poems aimed at young people, my reaction was that it would be tricky. Very few of the Irish poets, today or in the past, have branched out into writing for the young. I gave this unhelpful fact to the editor across the lunch table from me. Undaunted, she poured me some wine and urged me nevertheless to think about it. She told me how rich the Irish poetry tradition was. I sipped my wine and listened to her.

She was persuasive enough for me to go away saying I'd try. I still wasn't optimistic, though. I started visiting the Poetry Library in the South Bank Centre with the intention of reading my way through every Irish book there and making copies of any poem that might fit. I got a folder which I wrote Irish Poems on. It wasn't filling quickly. Then changes occurred in my life that took me away from London. The project got shelved. The originally generous deadline had to be extended further. I found myself reluctant to think of the anthology, mainly because I couldn't see any practical way to amass the material I needed.

Until I moved to Berlin, and discovered the library of the English Institute of the Free University there. Here was a fantastic collection of Irish poetry, old and new, English language and Irish. Day after day I went in and read my way through the relevant shelves. I kept having to replace the €5 card for the photocopier. I was discovering poems I didn't know existed and found myself more and more excited by the wealth of Irish poetry in the past. At the same time, my original doubts resurfaced. But, interestingly, I quickly realized it now didn't matter. I still wanted stuff that might speak to young people and this dictated my decision on which poems to photocopy, and which to leave. I asked myself if the poem I was reading might reach readers new to poetry. At the same time I was looking to discover poems that more mature people might remember and perhaps might not have seen in a while.

Shortly after this I left Berlin, and took my thick folder of photocopies to Ireland with me. In a house in Donegal I spread poems all over the floor, moving towards a final selection, looking at the same time for an order that seemed to make sense. I took to reading some of the poems aloud to my father, who was familiar with a lot of them. He was very happy that some of the older ones would see publication again and, like me, he was proud of the light that would be thrown on Ireland by such a gathering.

What was it that I noticed about these poems when I read them out? Their musical quality. Their narrative strength. The metaphorical richness of so many of them. The sense of mystery that many of us, children and adults, find so attractive. The world of fairies, for example, features prominently, and it was Yeats' early fairy poems 'The Stolen Child' and 'The Song of Wandering Aengus' (both represented here) that first drew me to poetry. As this suggests, folklore is often somewhere nearby, and the accompanying oral tradition. Some of the pieces included are actually songs, or have a second life in song, and I have a memory of my father singing one of them – Padraic Colum's 'She Moved through the Fair' – at the Feis in Derry when I was a child. There is a decent representation of poems in the Irish language, or translations or versions of such, and many of the English-language poems included draw on the older Irish tradition. The reader will also become a little familiar, in passing, with Irish history, and poetry is as good a way as any to encounter this.

To go back to my initial response, I am glad I was proved wrong, but the anthology I have come up with is very different from the one I was pessimistic about putting together at that initial lunch. It is a collection I feel will have an appeal across the ages, and will do so with a flavour of Ireland.

Matthew Sweeney, 2004

3

'Icham of Irlaunde'

Icham of Irlaunde
Ant of the holy londe
Of Irlande.

Gode sire, pray ich the,
For of saynte charite,
Come ant daunce wyt me
In Irelaunde.

Anon.
(early fourteenth century)

The Mystery

I am the wind which breathes upon the sea,
I am the wave of the ocean,
I am the murmur of the billows,
I am the ox of the seven combats,
I am the vulture upon the rocks,
I am a beam of the sun,
I am the fairest of plants,
I am the wild boar in valour,
I am a salmon in the water,
I am a lake in the plain,
I am a word of science,
I am the point of the lance of battle,
I am the God who created in the head the fire.
Who is it who throws light into the meeting
    on the mountain?
Who announces the ages of the moon?
Who teaches the place where couches the
    sun?
                                (If not I)

Amergin
Translated by Douglas Hyde

The Stolen Child

Where dips the rocky highland
Of Sleuth Wood in the lake,
There lies a leafy island
Where flapping herons wake
The drowsy water-rats;
There we've hid our faery vats,
Full of berries
And of reddest stolen cherries.
Come away, O human child!
To the waters and the wild
With a faery, hand in hand,
For the world's more full of weeping than
    you can understand.

Where the wave of moonlight glosses
The dim grey sands with light,
Far off by furthest Rosses
We foot it all the night,
Weaving olden dances,
Mingling hands and mingling glances
Till the moon has taken flight;
To and fro we leap

And chase the frothy bubbles,
While the world is full of troubles
And is anxious in its sleep.
Come away, O human child!
To the waters and the wild
With a faery, hand in hand,
For the world's more full of weeping than
  you can understand.

Where the wandering water gushes
From the hills above Glen-Car,
In pools among the rushes
That scarce could bathe a star,
We seek for slumbering trout
And whispering in their ears
Give them unquiet dreams;
Leaning softly out
From ferns that drop their tears
Over the young streams.
Come away, O human child!
To the waters and the wild
With a faery, hand in hand,
For the world's more full of weeping than
  you can understand.

Away with us he's going,
The solemn-eyed:
He'll hear no more the lowing
Of the calves on the warm hillside
Or the kettle on the hob
Sing peace into his breast,
Or see the brown mice bob
Round and round the oatmeal-chest.
For he comes, the human child,
To the waters and the wild
With a faery, hand in hand,
From a world more full of weeping than
*   he can understand.*

W. B. Yeats

The Fairies

Up the airy mountain,
  Down the rushy glen,
We daren't go a-hunting
  For fear of little men;
Wee folk, good folk,
  Trooping all together;
Green jacket, red cap,
  And white owl's feather!

Down along the rocky shore
  Some make their home,
They live on crispy pancakes
  Of yellow tide-foam;
Some in the reeds
  Of the black mountain-lake,
With frogs for their watchdogs,
  All night awake.

High on the hilltop
  The old King sits;
He is now so old and grey
  He's nigh lost his wits.
With a bridge of white mist
  Columbkill he crosses,
On his stately journeys
  From Slieveleague to Rosses;
Or going up with music,
  On cold starry nights,
To sup with the Queen
  Of the gay Northern Lights.

They stole little Bridget
  For seven years long;
When she came down again
  Her friends were all gone.
They took her lightly back,
  Between the night and morrow;
They thought that she was fast asleep,
  But she was dead with sorrow.
They have kept her ever since

Deep within the lake,
On a bed of flag-leaves,
  Watching till she wake.

By the craggy hillside,
  Through the mosses bare,
They have planted thorn-trees
  For pleasure here and there.
Is any man so daring
  As dig them up in spite?
He shall find their sharpest thorns
  In his bed at night.

Up the airy mountain
  Down the rushy glen,
We daren't go a-hunting,
  For fear of little men;
Wee folk, good folk,
  Trooping all together;
Green jacket, red cap,
  And white owl's feather!

William Allingham

Ardan Mór

As I was climbing Ardan Mór
From the shore of Sheelin lake
I met the herons coming down
Before the water's wake.

And they were talking in their flight
Of dreamy ways the herons go
When all the hills are withered up
Nor any waters flow.

Francis Ledwidge

The Making of Birds

God made Him birds in a pleasant humour;
    Tired of planets and suns was He.
He said: 'I will add a glory to Summer,
    Gifts for my creatures banished from Me!'

He had a thought and it set Him smiling
    Of the shape of a bird and its glancing head,
Its dainty air and its grace beguiling:
    'I will make feathers,' the Lord God said.

He made the robin; He made the swallow;
    His deft hands moulding the shape to His
       mood,
The thrush and lark and the finch to follow,
    And laughed to see that His work was good.

He Who has given men gift of laughter –
    Made in His image; He fashioned fit
The blink of the owl and the stork thereafter,
    The little wren and the long-tailed tit.

He spent in the making His wit and fancies;
    The wing-feathers He fashioned them strong;
Deft and dear as daisies and pansies,
    He crowned His work with the gift of song.

'Dearlings,' he said, 'make songs for My praises!'
    He tossed them loose to the sun and wind,
Airily sweet as pansies and daisies;
    He taught them to built a nest to their mind.

The dear Lord God of His glories weary –
    Christ our Lord had the heart of a boy –
Made him birds in a moment merry,
    Bade them soar and sing for His joy.

Katherine Tynan

Afterpeace

This wind that howls about our roof tonight
And tears live branches screaming from great
    trees
Tomorrow may have scarcely strength to
    ruffle
The rabbit's back to silver in the sun.

Patrick McDonagh

Cockles and Mussels

In Dublin's fair city,
Where the girls are so pretty,
I first set my eyes on sweet Mollie Malone.
She wheeled her wheelbarrow
Through streets broad and narrow,
Crying, 'Cockles and mussels, alive, alive, oh!

   'Alive, alive, oh!
   Alive, alive, oh!'
   Crying, 'Cockles and mussels, alive, alive, oh!'

She was a fishmonger,
But sure 'twas no wonder,
For so were her father and mother before.
And they both wheeled their barrow
Through streets broad and narrow,
Crying 'Cockles and mussels, alive, alive, oh!

   'Alive, alive, oh!
   Alive, alive, oh!'
   Crying, 'Cockles and mussels, alive, alive, oh!'

She died of a fever,
And none could relieve her,
And that was the end of sweet Mollie Malone.
But her ghost wheels her barrow
Through streets broad and narrow,
Crying, 'Cockles and mussels, alive, alive, oh!

'Alive, alive, oh!
Alive, alive, oh!'
Crying, 'Cockles and mussels, alive, alive, oh!'

Traditional

The Railway Children

When we climbed the slopes of the cutting
We were eye-level with the white cups
Of the telegraph poles and the sizzling wires.

Like lovely freehand they curved for miles
East and miles west beyond us, sagging
Under their burden of swallows.

We were small and thought we knew nothing
Worth knowing. We thought words travelled the wires
In the shiny pouches of raindrops,

Each one seeded full with the light
Of the sky, the gleam of the lines, and ourselves
So infinitesimally scaled

We could stream through the eye of a needle.

Seamus Heaney

from Tarry Flynn

On an apple-ripe September morning
Through the mist-chill fields I went
With a pitchfork on my shoulder
Less for use than for devilment.

The threshing mill was set up, I knew,
In Cassidy's haggard last night,
And we owed them a day at the threshing
Since last year. O it was delight

To be paying bills of laughter
And chaffy gossip in kind
With work thrown in to ballast
The fantasy-soaring mind.

As I crossed the wooden bridge I wondered
As I looked into the drain
If ever a summer morning should find me
Shovelling up eels again.

And I thought of the wasps' nest in the bank
And how I got chased one day
Leaving the drag and the scraw-knife behind,
How I covered my face with hay.

The wet leaves of the cocksfoot
Polished my boots as I
Went round by the glistening bog-holes
Lost in unthinking joy.

I'll be carrying bags today, I mused,
The best job at the mill
With plenty of time to talk of our loves
As we wait for the bags to fill.

Maybe Mary might call round . . .
And then I came to the haggard gate,
And I knew as I entered that I had come
Through fields that were part of no earthly estate.

Patrick Kavanagh

White Waves on the Water

White waves on the water,
Gold leaves on the tree,
As Mananan's daughter
Arose from the sea.

The bud and the blossom,
The fruit of the foam
From Ocean's dark bosom
Arose, from her home.

She came at your calling,
O winds of the world,
When the ripe fruit was falling
And the flowers unfurled.

She came at your crying
O creatures of earth
And the sound of your sighing
Made music and mirth.

She came at your keening
O dreamers of doom,
And your sleep had new dreaming
And splendour and bloom.

Joseph M. Plunkett

Deirín Dé

Deirín dé, deirín dé,
tá an gabhar donn ag labhairt sa bhfraoch;
deirín dé, deirín dé,
tá na lachain ag screadaigh sa bhféith.

Deirín dé, deirín dé,
gheobhaidh ba siar le héirí an lae,
deirín dé, deirín dé,
is rachaidh mo leanbh á bhfeighilt ar féar.

Deirín dé, deirín dé,
éireoidh gealach is rachaidh grian fé;
deirín dé, deirín dé,
is tusa mo leanbh is mo chuid den tsaol.

Deirín dé, deirín dé,
tá nead smólaí im chóifrín féin;
deirín dé, deirín dé,
tá, agus ór dom stóirín féin.

Deirín dé, deirín dé,
ligfead mo leanbh ag piocadh sméar,
deirín dé, deirín dé,
ach codladh go sámh go fáinne an lae.

Anon.

Deirín Dé

Deirín dé, deirín dé,
the blown goat calling in the heather,
deirín dé, deirín dé,
the ducks are squawking in the marsh.

Deirín dé, deirín dé,
cows go west at dawn of day,
deirín dé, deirín dé,
and my babe will mind them on the grass.

Deirín dé, deirín dé,
moon will rise and sun will set,
deirín dé, deirín dé,
and you are my babe and share of life.

Deirín dé, deirín dé,
a thrush's nest in my little press,
deirín dé, deirín dé,
yes, and gold for my little darling.

Deirín dé, deirín dé,
I'll let my babe out picking berries,
Deirín dé, deirín dé,
if he'll just sleep sound till the round of day.

Anon.
Translated by Thomas Kinsella

Buachaillín Bán

The buachaillín bawn he
Is going from me,
His spade he sold and his boots are on
He'll tramp his passage
Down to the seaside
And find a ship there some early dawn;
Soon he'll be sailing
The round white day-ring
To Amerikay, oh my buachailleen bawn.

The buachaillín bawn
The tall, the fair one,
His spade he sold and his boots are on,
In yellow leather
His hat a-feather
He's all for travelling to Boston Town
Farewell, my darling,
Away I'm faring
A coach and coachman you will see soon
With four white horses
To make their courses
Before your door, with the buachailleen bawn.

The buachaillín bawn
Fair one, O tall one
It's he went faring with three crowns or more;
A maiden met he,
Tall jack-a-dandy
     fared
It's he went forth with no crowns at all
A maiden met he
Tall jack-a-dandy
A farmer's daughter was his downfall.
Oh you must marry
With her you tarry
And leave the other you prate upon;
I've gold and riches
And hanging flitches
And all for you, Oh, my buachailleen bawn.

The buachailleen bawn
Has risen by dawn
He ploughs, he's mowing, all things to right
His only course is
Behind two horses
And naught to spend of a market night;
His breeches yellow
Would fit a fellow
Three times his size did he put them on;
Oh, high he married
The day he tarried
But low he lives now the buachailleen bawn.

Padraig Fallon

On a Dead Scholar

Dead is Lon
    Of Kilgarrow,
    O great sorrow!
Dead and gone.
Dire the dolour,
    Erin, here and past thy border,
    Dire the dolour and disorder,
To the schools and to the scholar,
    Since our Lon
    Is dead and gone.

Alfred Perceval Graves

The Hermit's Song

A hiding tuft, a green-barked yew tree
    Is my roof,
While nearby a great oak keeps me
    Tempest-proof.

I can pick my fruit from an apple
    Like an inn,
Or can fill my fist where hazels
    Shut me in.

A clear well beside me offers
    Best of drink,
And there grows a bed of cresses
    Near its brink.

Pigs and goats, the friendliest neighbours,
    Nestle near,
Wild swine come, or broods of badgers,
    Grazing deer.

All the gentry of the county
　　Come to call!
And the foxes come behind them,
　　Best of all.

To what meals the woods invite me
　　All about!
There are water, herbs and cresses,
　　Salmon, trout.

A clutch of eggs, sweet mast and honey
　　Are my meat,
Heathberries and whortleberries
　　For a sweet.

All that one could ask for comfort
　　Round me grows,
Three are hips and haws and strawberries,
　　Nuts and sloes.

And when summer spreads its mantle
    What a sight!
Marjoram and leeks and pignuts,
    Juicy, bright.

Dainty redbreasts briskly forage
    Every bush,
Round and round my hut there flutter
    Swallow, thrush.

Bees and beetles, music-makers,
    Croon and strum;
Geese pass over, duck in autumn,
    Dark streams hum.

Angry wren, officious linnet
    And blackcap,
All industrious, and the woodpeckers'
    Sturdy tap.

From the sea the gulls and herons
　　Flutter in,
While in upland heather rises
　　The grey hen.

In the year's most brilliant weather
　　Heifers low
Through green fields, not driven nor beaten,
　　Tranquil, slow.

In wreathed boughs the wind is whispering
　　Skies are blue,
Swans call, river water falling
　　Is calling too.

Anon.
Translated by Frank O'Connor

The Rath in Front of the Oak Wood

The *rath* in front of the oak wood
belonged to Bruidge, and Cathal,
belonged to Aedh, and Ailill,
belonged to Conaing, and Cuilíne
and to Mael Dúin before them
– all kings in their turn.
The *rath* survives; the kings
are covered in clay.

Anon.
Translated by Thomas Kinsella

He is coming, Adzed-Head

He is coming, Adzed-Head,
on the wild-headed sea
with cloak hollow-headed
and curve-headed staff.

He will chant false religion
at a bench facing east
and his people will answer
'Amen, amen.'

Anon.
Translated by Thomas Kinsella

Lament for Tadhg Cronin's Children

based on a poem by Aodhagán O Rathaille

That day the sails of the ship were torn
and a fog obscured the lawns.
In the whitewashed house the music stopped.
A spark jumped up at the gables
and the silk quilts on the bed caught fire.
They cry without tears –
their hearts cry –
for the three dead children.

Christ God neglect them not
nor leave them in the ground!

They were ears of corn!
They were apples!
They were three harpstrings!
And now their limbs lie underground
and the black beetle walks across their faces.
I, too, cry without tears –
my heart cries –
for the three dead children.

Michael Hartnett

The Ballad of Father Gilligan

The old priest Peter Gilligan
  Was weary night and day;
For half his flock were in their beds,
  Or under green sods lay.

Once, while he nodded on a chair,
  At the moth-hour of eve,
Another poor man sent for him,
  And he began to grieve.

'I have no rest, nor joy, nor peace,
  For people die and die;'
And after cried he, 'God forgive!
  My body spake, not I!'

He knelt, and leaning on the chair
  He prayed and fell asleep;
And the moth-hour went from the fields,
  And stars began to peep.

They slowly into millions grew,
  And leaves shook in the wind;
And God covered the world with shade,
  And whispered to mankind.

Upon the time of sparrow chirp
   When the moths came once more,
The old priest Peter Gilligan
   Stood upright on the floor.

'*Mavrone, mavrone!* the man has died,
   While I slept on the chair;'
He roused his horse out of its sleep,
   And rode with little care.

He rode now as he never rode,
   By rocky lane and fen;
The sick man's wife opened the door:
   'Father! you come again!'

'And is the poor man dead?' he cried.
   'He died an hour ago,'
The old priest Peter Gilligan
   In grief swayed to and fro.

'When you were gone, he turned and died
   As merry as a bird.'
The old priest Peter Gilligan
   He knelt him at that word.

'He who hath made the night of stars
　　For souls, who tire and bleed,
Sent one of His great angels down
　　To help me in my need.

'He who is wrapped in purple robes,
　　With planets in His care,
Had pity on the least of things
　　Asleep upon a chair.'

W. B. Yeats

Jesus and the Sparrows

Imbu maccán cóic blíadnae
    Ísu macc Dé bí,
sénais dá uiscén deac,
    arrus-fí di chrí.

Delbais dá énán deac –
    Paisir a n-anmann –
Dia Sapaite dos-géni
    di chrí cen madmann.

Con-saíd alaile Iudea
    Isu mac Dé máir;
dochum a aiti Ioseph
    don-indnacht ar láim.

'Ergair do macc, a Ioseph;
    ní maith a ndo-gní;
Dia Sapaite dos-rigni
    delba én di chrí.'

Con-ort Ísu a dí bais,
     a guthán ro-cloth;
fiad a súilib – ségdae rath –
     ind énán, fos-mboth.

Ro-clos guthán cain inmain
     for giun Ísu glain:
'Ar fessid ciab dergéni
     airciub do for ndaim.'

Fásaig alaile do túaith,
     Ba hamrae a scél,
Ro-clossa for luamain
     Garmann inna n-én.

                    Anon.

The Boyhood of Christ

after Jesus and the Sparrows

When he was barely five
Jesus, the Son of God,
blessed twelve water puddles
He moulded out of clay.

He made a dozen birds
– the kind we call the sparrow –
He made them on the Sabbath,
perfect, out of clay.

A Jew there criticized Him
– Jesus, the Son of God! –
and to His father Joseph
took Him by the hand.

'Joseph, correct your son,
he has committed wrong.
He made clay shapes of birds
upon the Sabbath day.'

Jesus clapped His palms
His little voice was heard.
Before their eyes – a miracle –
the little birds flew off.

The sweet, beloved voice was heard
from the mouth of Jesus pure:
'So they will know who made you
off with you to your homes.'

A man who was there told everyone
the wonderful affair
and overhead they all could hear
the singing of the birds.

Anon.
Translated by Thomas Kinsella

The Blackbird by Belfast Lough

What little throat
Has framed that note?
What gold beak shot
   It far away?
A blackbird on
His leafy throne
Tossed it alone
   Across the bay.

Anon.

Translated by Frank O'Connor

The Day Set for Our Wedding

after the Irish

The day is set for our wedding
The town was full of horses,
There were priests and brothers murmuring
The words of the marriage service,
The feast upon the table,
The harp and charming fiddle,
Little the bridesmaids thought then
That they'd lay out my darling.

Take tidings to my people
That the sea has widowed me
And that my love who lightened
The air at any meeting,
Who would have been well mated
With the King of France's daughter
Is heavy on the bed
They decked out for our bridal.

The monsters have his eyes
And crabs the mouth that kissed me,
His two, bright, white hands
Devoured by the great salmon,
His curls tangled with salt
Are all the sea has spared me –
And may they rot, the botches
Who built the boat that drowned him.

Donagh MacDonagh

'S Í Bláth Geal Na Sméar Í

'S í bláth geal na smear í,
's í bláth deas na sú craobh í,
's í planda b'fhearr méin mhaith
le hamharc do shúl;
's í mo chuisle, 's í mo rún í,
's í bláth na n-úll gcumhra í,
is samhradh ins an fhuacht í
idir Nollaig is Cáisc.

Anon.

She's the Blackberry-Flower

She's the blackberry-flower,
the fine raspberry-flower,
she's the plant of best breeding
   your eyes could behold:
she's my darling and dear,
my fresh apple-tree flower,
she is summer in the cold
   between Christmas and Easter.

Anon.
Translated by Thomas Kinsella

A Mill

Two leaps the water from its race
    Made to the brook below,
The first leap it was curving glass,
    The second bounding snow.

William Allingham

Winter

Scél lem dúib:
  dordaid dam,
snigid gaim
  ro fáith sam.

Gáeth ard úar,
  ísel grían;
gair a rrith,
  ruithech rían.

Rorúad raith,
  ro cleth cruth,
ro gab gnáth
  giugrann guth.

ro gab úacht
  etti én;
aigrid ré –
  é mo scél.

Anon.

Season Song

Here's a song –
stags give tongue
winter snows
summer goes.

High cold blow
sun is low
brief his day
seas give spray.

Fern clumps redden
shapes are hidden
wild geese raise
wonted cries.

Cold now girds
wings of birds
icy time –
that's my rime.

Anon.
Translated by Flann O'Brien

To Morfydd

A voice on the winds,
A voice by the waters,
  Wanders and cries:
Oh! what are the winds?
And what are the waters?
  Mine are your eyes!

Western the winds are,
And western the waters,
  Where the light lies:
Oh! what are the winds?
And what are the waters?
  Mine are your eyes!

Cold, cold, grow the winds,
And wild grow the waters,
  Where the sun dies:
Oh! what are the winds?
And what are the waters?
  Mine are your eyes!

And down the night winds,
And down the night waters,
  The music flies:
Oh! what are the winds?
And what are the waters?
Cold be the winds,
And wild be the waters,
  So mine be your eyes!

Lionel Johnson

A Vision of Connaught in the Thirteenth Century

I walked entranced
         Through a land of Morn;
The sun, with wondrous excess of light,
         Shone down and glanced
                  Over seas of corn
And lustrous gardens aleft and right.
         Even in the clime
                  Of resplendent Spain,
Beams no such sun upon such a land;
         But it was the time,
                  'Twas in the reign,
Of Cáhal Mór of the Wine-red Hand.

Anon. stood nigh
By my side a man
Of princely aspect and port sublime
Him queried I –
'O my Lord and Khan,
What clime is this, and what golden time?'
When he – 'The clime
Is a clime to praise,
The Clime is Erin's, the green and bland;
And it is the time,
These be the days,
Of Cáhal Mór of the Wine-red Hand!'

Then saw I thrones,
        And circling fires,
And a Dome rose near me, as by a spell,
        Whence flowed the tones
        Of silver lyres,
And many voices in wreathèd swell;
        And their thrilling chime
        Fell on mine ears
As the heavenly hymn of an angel-band –
        'It is now the time,
        These be the years,
Of Cáhal Mór of the Wine-red Hand.'

I sought the hall,
           And, behold! – a change
From light to darkness, from joy to woe!
      King, nobles, all,
           Looked aghast and strange;
The minstrel-group sate in dumbest show!
      Had some great crime
           Wrought this dread amaze,
This terror? None seemed to understand
      'Twas then the time,
           We were in the days,
Of Cáhal Mór of the Wine-red Hand.

I again walked forth;
But lo! the sky
Showed fleckt with blood, and an alien sun
Glared from the north,
And there stood on high,
Amid his shorn beams, a skeleton!
It was by the stream
Of the castled Maine,
One Autumn eve, in the Teuton's land,
That I dreamed this dream
Of the time and reign
Of Cáhal Mór of the Wine-red Hand!

James Clarence Mangan

Claudy

for Harry Barton – a song

The Sperrins surround it, the Faughan flows by,
at each end of Main Street the hills and the sky,
the small town of Claudy at ease in the sun
last July in the morning, a new day begun.

How peaceful and pretty if the moment could stop,
McIlhenny is straightening things in his shop,
and his wife is outside serving petrol, and then
a girl takes a cloth to a big windowpane.

And McCloskey is taking the weight off his feet,
and McClelland and Miller are sweeping the street,
and, delivering milk at the Beaufort Hotel,
young Temple's enjoying his first job quiet well.

And Mrs McLaughlin is scrubbing her floor,
and Artie Hone's crossing the street to a door,
and Mrs Brown, looking around for her cat,
goes off up an entry – what's strange about that?

Not much – but before she comes back to the road
that strange car parked outside her house will explode,
and all of the people I've mentioned outside
will be waiting to die or already have died.

An explosion too loud for your eardrums to bear,
and young children squealing like pigs in the square,
and all faces chalk-white and streaked with bright red,
and the glass and the dust and the terrible dead.

For an old lady's legs are ripped off, and the head
of a man's hanging open, and still he's not dead.
He is screaming for mercy, and his son stands and stares
and stares, and then suddenly, quick, disappears.

And Christ, little Katherine Aiken is dead,
and Mrs McLaughlin is pierced through the head.
Meanwhile to Dungiven the killers are gone,
and they're finding it hard to get through on the phone.

James Simmons

Poem from a Three-year-old

And will the flowers die?

And will the people die?

And every day do you grow old, do I
grow old, no I'm not old, do
flowers grow old?

Old things – do you throw them out?

Do you throw old people out?

And how you know a flower that's old?

The petals fall, the petals fall from flowers,
and do the petals fall from people too,
every day more petals fall until the
floor where I would like to play I
want to play is covered with old
flowers and people all the same
together lying there with petals fallen
on the dirty floor I want to play
the floor you come and sweep
with the huge broom.

The dirt you sweep, what happens that,
what happens all the dirt you sweep
from flowers and people, what
happens all the dirt? Is all the
dirt what's left of flowers and
people, all the dirt there in a
heap under the huge broom that
sweeps everything away?

Why you work so hard, why brush
and sweep to make a heap of dirt?

And who will bring new flowers?

And who will bring new people? Who will
bring new flowers to put in water
where no petals fall on to the
floor where I would like to
play? Who will bring new flowers
that will not hang their heads
like tired old people wanting sleep?
Who will bring new flowers that
do not split and shrivel every
day? And if we have new flowers,
will we have new people too to
keep the flowers alive and give
them water?

And will the new young flowers die?

And will the new young people die?

And why?

Brendan Kennelly

A Christmas Childhood

I

One side of the potato-pits was white with frost –
How wonderful that was, how wonderful!
And when we put our ears to the paling-post
The music that came out was magical.

The light between the ricks of hay and straw
Was a hole in Heaven's gable. An apple tree
With its December-glinting fruit we saw –
O you, Eve, were the world that tempted me

To eat the knowledge that grew in clay
And death the germ within it! Now and then
I can remember something of the gay
Garden that was childhood's. Again

The tracks of cattle to a drinking-place,
A green stone lying sideways in a ditch
Or any common sight the transfigured face
Of a beauty that the world did not touch.

II

My father played the melodeon
Outside at our gate;
There were stars in the morning east
And they danced to his music.

Across the wild bogs his melodeon called
To Lennons and Callans.
As I pulled on my trousers in a hurry
I knew some strange thing had happened.

Outside in the cow-house my mother
Made the music of milking;
The light of her stable lamp was a star
And the frost of Bethlehem made it twinkle.

A water-hen screeched in the bog,
Mass-going feet
Crunched the wafer-ice on the potholes,
somebody wistfully twisted the bellows wheel.

My child poet picked out the letters
On the grey stone,
In silver the wonder of a Christmas townland,
The winking glitter of a frosty dawn.

Cassiopeia was over
Cassidy's hanging hill,
I looked and three whin bushes rode across
The horizon – the Three Wise Kings.

An old man passing said:
'Can't he make it talk' –
The melodeon. I hid in the doorway
And tightened the belt of my box-pleated coat.

I nicked six nicks on the door-post
With my penknife's big blade –
There was a little one for cutting tobacco.
And I was six Christmases of age.

My father played the melodeon,
My mother milked the cows,
And I had a prayer like a white rose pinned
On the Virgin Mary's blouse.

Patrick Kavanagh

The Vikings

Bitter the wind tonight,
combing the sea's hair white:
from the North, no need to fear
the proud sea-coursing warrior.

Anon.
Translated by John Montague

The Son of the King of Moy

The son of the king of Moy in midsummer
Found a girl in the greenwood.
She gave him black fruit from thornbushes.
She gave an armful of strawberries on rushes.

Anon.
Translated by Myles Dillon

The Song of Wandering Aengus

I went out to the hazel wood,
Because a fire was in my head,
And cut and peeled a hazel wand,
And hooked a berry to a thread;
And when white moths were on the wing,
And moth-like stars were flickering out,
I dropped the berry in a stream
And caught a little silver trout.

When I had laid it on the floor
I went to blow the fire aflame,
But something rustled on the floor,
And some one called me by my name:
It had become a glimmering girl
With apple blossom in her hair
Who called me by my name and ran
And faded through the brightening air.

Though I am old with wandering
Through hollow lands and hilly lands,
I will find out where she has gone,
And kiss her lips and take her hands;
And walk among long dappled grass,
And pluck till time and times are done
The silver apples of the moon,
The golden apples of the sun.

W. B. Yeats

The Enchanted Island

To Rathlin's Isle I chanced to sail,
    When summer breezes softly blew,
And there I heard so sweet a tale,
    That oft I wished it could be true.
They said, at eve, when rude winds sleep,
    And hushed is every turbid swell,
A mermaid rises from the deep,
    And sweetly tunes her magic shell.

And while she plays, rock, dell, and cave,
    In dying falls the sound retain,
As if some choral spirits gave
    Their aid to swell her witching strain.
Then summoned by that dulcet note,
    Uprising to th' admiring view,
A fairy island seems to float
    With tints of many a gorgeous hue.

And glittering fanes, and lofty towers,
    All on this fairy isle are seen;
And waving trees, and shady bowers,
    With more than mortal verdure green.
And as it moves, the western sky
    Glows with a thousand varying rays;
And the calm sea, tinged with each dye,
    Seems like a golden flood of blaze.

They also say, if earth or stone,
    From verdant Erin's hallowed land,
Were on this magic island thrown,
    Forever fixed, it then would stand.
But, when for this, some little boat
    In silence ventures from the shore –
The mermaid sinks – hushed is the note,
    The fairy isle is seen no more!

Anon.

The Shell

And then I pressed the shell
Close to my ear
And listened well,
And straightway like a bell
Came low and clear
The slow, sad murmur of far distant seas,
Whipped by an icy breeze
Upon a shore
Wind-swept and desolate.
It was a sunless strand that never bore
The footprint of a man,
Nor felt the weight
Since time began
Of any human quality or stir
Save what the dreary winds and waves incur.
And in the hush of waters was the sound
Of pebbles rolling round,
Forever rolling with a hollow sound.
And bubbling sea-weeds as the waters go
Swish to and fro
Their long, cold tentacles of slimy grey.
There was no day,
Nor ever came a night
Setting the stars alight

To wonder at the moon:
Was twilight only and the frightened croon,
Smitten to whimpers, of the dreary wind
And waves that journeyed blind –
And when I loosed my ear – oh, it was sweet
To hear a cart go jolting down the street!

James Stephens

A Drover

To Meath of the pastures,
    From wet hills by the sea,
Through Leitrim and Longford
    Go my cattle and me.

I hear in the darkness
    Their slipping and breathing.
I name them the by-ways
    They're to pass without heeding.

Then the wet, winding roads,
    Brown bogs with black water;
And my thoughts on white ships
    And the King o' Spain's daughter.

O farmer, strong farmer!
    You can spend at the fair,
But your face you must turn
    To your crops and your care.

And soldiers, red soldiers!
    You've seen many lands;
But you walk two and two,
    And by captain's commands.

O the smell of the beasts,
    The wet wind in the morn,
And the proud and hard earth
    Never broken for corn!

And the crowds at the fair,
    The herds loosened and blind,
Loud words and dark faces
    And the wild blood behind.

(O strong men with your best
    I would strive breast to breast
I could quiet your herds
    With my words, with my words!)

I will bring you, my kine,
    Where there's grass to the knee;
But you'll think of scant croppings
    Harsh with salt of the sea.

Padraic Colum

Mo-chean Do Theacht, A Scadáin

Mo-chean do theacht, a scadáin;
  druid liom, a dhaltáin uasail;
do chéad beatha 's do shláinte.
  do thuillis fáilte uaimse.

Dar láimh m'athar, a scadáin,
  gé maith bradáin na Bóinne,
duit do dhealbhas an duainse
  ós tú is uaisle 's is óige.

A fhir is comhghlan colann
  nach ndéanann comann bréige,
cara mar thú ní bhfuaras;
  bá bíom sarach fá chéile.

Dá bhféachdaois uaisle Banbha
  cia is mó tarbha den triúrsa:
is rí ar gach iasc an scadán
  idir bhradán is liúsa.

Is é ar bhféachain gach cósta
    go crích bhóchna na Gréige,
iasc is uaisle ná an scadán
    ní bhfuair Canán Chinn tSléibhe.

A scadáin shéimhe shúgaigh,
    a chinn chúmhdaigh an Chárghais,
a mhic ghrádhaigh mo charad,
    liom is fada go dtángais.

Gé mór do thuit a-nuraidh
    ded ghaol bhunaidh fán méis-se,
ná cuimhnigh fíoch ná fala,
    ós tú cara na cléire.

A scadáin shailltigh shoilbhir
    nach bíonn go doilbhir dúinte,
liomsa do theacht nín hanait,
    súil ar charaid an tsúilse.

Anon.

Hail, Herring! You've come!

Hail, herring! You've come!
    My fine son, come close.
Your health! A hundred greetings!
    You well deserve our welcome.

By my father's hand, herring,
    though Boyne salmon are fine
I made this poem for you,
    most noble and most fresh.

Sir, whose wholesome body
    gives no lying promise,
I have found no friend like you;
    let nothing mean divide us.

Let Banba's best consider
    the worthiest of these three:
over salmon, over pike,
    herring is king of fish.

When he studied every coast
    to the Greek land's ocean-edge
Canán Cinn tSléibhe could not find
    a nobler fish than the herring.

Herring, gentle and jovial,
    our mainstay in time of Lent,
my friends' favourite son,
    it was long until you came.

Though many of your close kin
    fell last year across this plate,
brood not in anger or spite,
    you, that are friend to poets.

Herring, salty, serene,
    not shut in self or sour,
your coming causes no pang!
    My eye rests on a friend.

Anon.
Translated by Thomas Kinsella

Heaven—Haven

a nun takes the veil

I have desired to go
　　Where springs not fail,
To fields where flies no sharp and sided hail
　　And a few lilies blow.

　　And I have asked to be
　　Where no storms come,
Where the green swell is in the havens dumb,
　　And out of the swing of the sea.

Gerard Manley Hopkins

Pied Beauty

Glory be to God for dappled things –
    For skies of couple-colour as a brinded cow;
        For rose-moles all in stipple upon trout that swim;
Fresh-firecoal chestnut-falls; finches' wings;
    Landscape plotted and pieced – fold, fallow and
        plough;
        And áll trádes, their gear and tackle and trim.

All things counter, original, spare, strange;
    Whatever is fickle, freckled (who knows how?)
        With swift, slow; sweet, sour; adazzle, dim;
He fathers-forth whose beauty is past change:
        Praise him.

Gerard Manley Hopkins

Cúl An Tí

Tá Tír na nÓg ar chúl an tí,
   Tír álainn trína chéile,
Lucht ceithre chos ag siúl na slí
   Gan bróga orthu ná léine,
   Gan Béarla acu ná Gaeilge.

Ach fásann clóca ar gach droim
   Sa tír seo trína chéile,
Is labhartar teanga ar chúl an tí
   Nár thuig aon fhear ach Aesop,
   Is tá sé siúd sa chré anois.

Tá cearca ann is ál sicín,
   Is lacha righin mhothaolach,
Is gadhar mór dubh mar namhaid sa tír
   Ag drannadh le gach éinne,
   Is cat ag crú na gréine.

Sa chúinne thiar tá banc dramhaíl'
   Is iontaisí an tsaoil ann,
Coinnleoir, búclaí, seanhata tuí,
   Is trúmpa balbh néata,
   Is citeal bán mar ghé ann.

Is ann a thagann tincéirí
   Go naofa, trína chéile,
Tá gaol acu le cúl an tí,
   Is bíd ag iarraidh déirce
   Ar chúl gach tí in Éirinn.

Ba mhaith liom bheith ar chúl an tí
   Sa doircheacht go déanach
Go bhfeicinn ann ar chuairt gealaí
   An t-ollaimhín sin Aesop
   Is é ina phúca léannta.

Sean O'Riordain

Behind the House

The Land of Youth's behind the house,
    A lovely, mixed-up country,
Four-footed folk walking the paths
    With no shoes or shirts on,
    With no English or Irish.

But a cloak grows on every back
    In this higgledy-piggledy country
And they speak a language behind the house
    That no one knew but Aesop
    And he's in the clay now.

Hens are there, and a clutch of chickens,
    And a simple stubborn duck,
And a big black hound like a hostile invader
    Snarling at everybody,
    And a cat milking the sun.

In the corner you'll find a rubbish dump
    Hoarding all life's wonders,
Candlesticks, buckles, an old straw hat,
    And a neat, dumb Jew's harp,
    And a white kettle like a goose.

It's there the tinkers hang about
    Saintly, all mixed up.
They're at home behind the house
    And can be found begging
    Behind every house in Ireland.

I'd like to be behind the house
    In the dark, very late
To see, on a visit of the moon,
    That little master, Aesop,
    Now a learned pooka.

Sean O'Riordain
Translated by Matthew Sweeney

I Saw Magic on a
Green Country Road . . .

I saw magic on a green country road –
That old woman, a bag of sticks her load,

Blackly down to her thin feet a fringed shawl,
A rosary of bone on her horned hand,
A flight of curlews scribing by her head,
And ashtrees combing with their frills her hair.

Her eyes, wet sunken holes pierced by an awl,
Must have deciphered her adoring land:
And curlews, no longer lean birds, instead
Become ten scarlet comets in the air.

Some incantation from her canyoned mouth,
Irish, English, blew frost along the ground,
And even though the wind was from the south
The ashleaves froze without an ashleaf sound.

Michael Hartnett

A Piper

A piper in the street today,
Set up, and tuned, and started to play,
And away, away, away on the tide
Of his music we started; on every side
Doors and windows were opened wide,
And men left down their work and came,
And women with petticoats coloured like flame,
And little bare feet that were blue with cold,
Went dancing back to the age of gold,
And all the world went gay, went gay,
For half an hour in the street today.

Seumas O'Sullivan

The Friar of Orders Grey

I am a friar of orders grey:
As down the valley I take my way,
   I pull not blackberry, haw or hip,
   Good store of venison does fill my scrip:
My long bead-roll I merrily chaunt,
Where'er I walk, no money I want;
And why I'm so plump the reason I'll tell –
Who leads a good life is sure to live well.
   What baron or squire
   Or knight of the shire
Lives half so well as a holy friar!

After supper, of heaven I dream,
But that is fat pullet and clouted cream.
   Myself, by denial, I mortify
   With a dainty bit of a warden pie:
   I'm clothed in sackcloth for my sin:
   With old sack wine I'm lined within:
A chirping cup is my matin song,
And the vesper bell is my bowl's ding-dong.
   What baron or squire
   Or knight of the shire
Lives half so well as a holy friar!

John O'Keefe

Beatha An Scoláire

Aoibhinn beatha an scoláire
    bhíos ag déanamh a léighinn;
is follas díbh, a dhaoine,
    gurab dó is aoibhne in Éirinn.

Gan smacht ríogh ná rófhlatha
    ná tighearna dá threise
gan chuid cíosa ag caibidil,
    gan moichéirghe, gan meirse.

Moichéirghe ná aodhaireacht
    ní thabhair uadha choidhche,
's ní mó do-bheir dá aire
    fear na faire san oidhche.

Do-bheir sé greas ar tháiplis,
    is ar chláirsigh go mbinne,
nó fós greas eile ar shuirghe
    is ar chumann mná finne.

Maith biseach a sheisrighe
   ag teacht tosaigh an earraigh;
is é is crannghail dá sheisrigh
   lán a ghlaice de pheannaibh.

Anon.

The Scholar's Life

Sweet is the scholar's life,
   busy about his studies,
the sweetest lot in Ireland
   as all of you know well.

No king or prince to rule him
   nor lord however mighty,
no rent to the chapterhouse,
   no drudging, no dawn-rising.

Dawn-rising or shepherding
   never required of him,
no need to take his turn
   as watchman in the night.

He spends a while at chess,
   and a while with the pleasant harp
and a further while wooing
   and winning lovely women.

His horse-team hale and hearty
  at the first coming of spring;
the harrow for his team
  is a fistful of pens.

Anon.
Translated by Thomas Kinsella

Pangur Bán

*written by a student of the monastery of Carinthia
on a copy of St Paul's Epistles*

I and Pangur Bán, my cat,
'Tis a like task we are at:
Hunting mice is his delight,
Hunting words I sit all night.

Better far than praise of men
'Tis to sit with book and pen;
Pangur bears me no ill will,
He too plies his simple skill.

'Tis a merry thing to see
At our tasks how glad are we,
When at home we sit and find
Entertainment to our mind.

Oftentimes a mouse will stray
In the hero Pangur's way;
Oftentimes my keen thought set
Takes a meaning in its net.

'Gainst the wall he sets his eye
Full and fierce and sharp and sly;
'Gainst the wall of knowledge I
All my little wisdom try.

When a mouse darts from its den,
Oh how glad is Pangur then!
Oh what gladness do I prove
When I solve the doubts I love!

So in peace our tasks we ply,
Pangur Bán, my cat, and I;
In our arts we find our bliss,
I have mine and he has his.

Practice every day has made
Pangur perfect in his trade;
I get wisdom day and night
Turning darkness into light.

Anon.
Translated by Robin Flower

The Fiddler of Dooney

When I play on my fiddle in Dooney,
Folk dance like a wave of the sea;
My cousin is priest in Kilvarnet,
My brother in Mocharabuiee.

I passed my brother and cousin:
They read in their books of prayer;
I read in my book of songs
I bought at the Sligo fair.

When we come at the end of time
To Peter sitting in state,
He will smile on the three old spirits,
But call me first through the gate;

For the good are always the merry,
Save by an evil chance,
And the merry love the fiddle,
And the merry love to dance:

And when the folk there spy me,
They will all come up to me,
With 'Here is the Fiddler of Dooney!'
And dance like a wave of the sea.

W. B. Yeats

The Finest Music

Once, as they rested on a chase, a debate arose among the Fianna-Finn as to what was the finest music in the world.

'Tell us that,' said Fionn, turning to Oisin.

'The cuckoo calling from the tree that is highest in the hedge,' cried his merry son.

'A good sound,' said Fionn. 'And you, Oscar,' he asked, 'what is to your mind the finest of music?'

'The top of music is the ring of a spear on a shield,' cried the stout lad.

'It is a good sound,' said Fionn.

And the other champions told their delight: the belling of a stag across water, the baying of a tuneful pack heard in the distance, the song of a lark, the laughter of a gleeful girl or the whisper of a moved one.

'They are good sounds all,' said Fionn.

'Tell us, chief,' one ventured, 'what do you think?'

'The music of what happens,' said great Fionn, 'that is the finest music in the world.'

James Stephens

The Four Travellers

Four travellers sat one winter's night
    At my father's board so free;
And he asked them why they left their land,
    And why they crossed the sea?

One said for bread, and one for gold,
    And one for a cause of strife;
And one he came for a lost love's sake,
    To lead a stranger's life.

They dwelt among our hamlets long,
    They learned each mountain way;
They shared our sports in the woodlands green,
    And by the crags so gay –

And they were brave by flood and fell,
    And they were blithe in hall;
But he that led the stranger's life,
    Was blithest of them all.

Some said the grief of his youth had passed,
    Some said his love grew cold;
But nought I know if this were so,
    For the tale was never told.

His mates they found both homes and friends,
    Their heads and hearts to rest;
We saw their flocks and fields increase,
    But we loved *him* still the best.

Now he that came to seek for bread,
    Is lord of my father's land;
And he that fled so far from strife,
    Hath a goodly household band.

And he that sought the gold alone,
    Hath wedded my sister fair;
And the oaks are green and the pastures wide,
    By their pleasant homesteads there.

But when they meet by the winter fire,
  Or beneath the bright woodbine;
Their talk is yet of a whelming stream
  And a brave life given for mine;

For a grave by our mountain river side,
  Grows green this many a year –
Where the flower of the four sleeps evermore,
  And I am a stranger here.

Frances Brown

The Croppy Boy

It was early, early in the spring,
The birds did whistle and sweetly sing,
Changing their notes from tree to tree
And the song they sang was 'Old Ireland Free'.

It was early, early in the night,
The Yeoman cavalry gave me a fright,
The Yeoman cavalry was my downfall
And I was taken by Lord Cornwall.

It was in the coach house that I was laid
And in the parlour that I was tried.
My sentence passed and my courage low
As to Duncannon I was forced to go.

As I was going up Wexford Street
My own first cousin I chanced to meet.
My own first cousin did me betray
And for one bare guinea swore my life away.

As I was passing my father's door
My brother William stood in the door,
My aged father stood there before
And my own dear mother her hair she tore.

As I was going up Wexford Hill
Oh who would blame me to cry my fill?
I looked behind and I looked before
And my own dear mother I shall ne'er see more.

As I was standing on the scaffold high
My own dear father was standing nigh.
My own dear father did me deny
And the name he gave me was 'The Croppy Boy'.

It was in Duncannon this young man died
And in Duncannon his body was laid.
Now all good people that do pass by
O spare a tear for 'The Croppy Boy'.

Anon.

A Dream

I heard the dogs howl in the moonlight night;
I went to the window to see the sight;
All the Dead that ever I knew
Going one by one and two by two.

On they pass'd, and on they pass'd;
Townfellows all, from first to last;
Born in the moonlight of the lane,
Quench'd in the heavy shadow again.

Schoolmates marching as when we play'd
At soldiers once – but now more staid;
Those were the strangest sight to me
Who were drown'd, I knew, in the awful sea.

Straight and handsome folk; bent and weak, too;
Some that I loved, and gasp'd to speak to;
Some but a day in their churchyard bed;
Some that I had not known were dead.

A long, long crowd – where each seem'd lonely,
Yet of them all there was one, one only,
Raised a head or look'd my way:
She linger'd a moment – she might not stay.

How long since I saw that fair pale face!
Ah! Mother dear! might I only place
My head on thy breast, a moment to rest,
While thy hand on my tearful cheek were prest!

On, on, a moving bridge they made
Across the moon-stream, from shade to shade,
Young and old, women and men;
Many long-forget, but remember'd then.

William Allingham

In Memory of My Mother

I do not think of you lying in the wet clay
Of a Monaghan graveyard; I see
You walking down a lane among the poplars
On your way to the station, or happily

Going to second Mass on a summer Sunday –
You meet me and you say:
'Don't forget to see about the cattle –'
Among your earthiest words the angels stray.

And I think of you walking along a headland
Of green oats in June,
So full of repose, so rich with life –
And I see us meeting at the end of a town

On a fair day by accident, after
The bargains are all made and we can walk
Together through the shops and stalls and markets
Free in the oriental streets of thought.

Oh you are not lying in the wet clay,
For it is a harvest evening now and we
Are piling up the ricks against the moonlight
And you smile up at us – eternally.

Patrick Kavanagh

A Cradle Song

O, men from the fields!
Come gently within.
Tread softly, softly,
O! men coming in.

Mavourneen is going
From me and from you,
Where Mary will fold him
With mantle of blue!

From reek of the smoke
And cold of the floor,
And the peering of things
Across the half-door.

O, men from the fields!
Soft, softly come thro'.
Mary puts round him
Her mantle of blue.

Padraic Colum

A Little Boy in the Morning

He will not come, and still I wait.
He whistles at another gate
Where angels listen. Ah, I know
He will not come, yet if I go
How shall I know he did not pass
Barefooted in the flowery grass?

The moon leans on one silver horn
Above the silhouettes of morn,
And from their nest-sills finches whistle
Or stooping pluck the downy thistle.
How is the morn so gay and fair
Without his whistling in its air?

The world is calling, I must go.
How shall I know he did not pass
Barefooted in the shining grass?

Francis Ledwidge

The Cat and the Moon

The cat went here and there
And the moon spun round like a top,
And the nearest kin of the moon,
The creeping cat, looked up.
Black Minnaloushe stared at the moon,
For, wander and wail as he would,
The pure cold light in the sky
Troubled his animal blood.
Minnaloushe runs in the grass
Lifting his delicate feet.
Do you dance, Minnaloushe, do you dance?
When two close kindred meet,
What better than call a dance?
Maybe the moon may learn,
Tired of that courtly fashion,
A new dance turn.
Minnaloushe creeps through the grass
From moonlit place to place,
The sacred moon overhead
Has taken a new phase.
Does Minnaloushe know that his pupils
Will pass from change to change,
And that from round to crescent,

From crescent to round they range?
Minnaloushe creeps through the grass
Alone, important and wise,
And lifts to the changing moon
His changing eyes.

W. B. Yeats

A Strong Wind

All day a strong wind blew
Across the green and brown from Kerry.
The leaves hurrying, two
By three, over the road, collected
In chattering groups. New berry
Dipped with old branch. Careful insects
Flew low behind their hedges.
Held back by her pretty petticoat,
Butterfly struggled. A bit of
Paper, on which a schoolgirl had written
'Máire loves Jimmy', jumped up
Into a tree. Tapping in haste,
The wind was telegraphing, hundreds
Of miles. All Ireland raced.

Austin Clarke

Halloween

It is Halloween. Turnip Head
Will soon be given his face,
A slit, two triangles, a hole.
His brains litter the table top.
A candle stub will be his soul.

Michael Longley

Pumpkinhead

If I stand at our fence
I can watch my brother
setting off for school.
It took him all last night
to carve the pumpkin on his head.
From here, he looks hilarious
with that huge orange head
and a flowing white sheet
covering the rest of him.
He carries his book-bag
just like any other school day
and walks along humming,
up to the bus stop.
Will he sit on the bus
with a pumpkin on his head?
Yes, he will.
He'll live inside there all day –
he measured the grinning mouth
and it is big enough
to pass a spoon and fork
and a candy bar into.
I lean over our fence
but he's just a little orange dot.

Julie O'Callaghan

Gates

We're a people who do not love gates, we
are lovers of gaps,
all sorts of oddly-shaped gaps,
gaps in the crochet of lime-stone walls,
gaps in the clouds and the hills,
we are lovers of space,
and our only concession to gates is
a bush or a broken old bed
that creaks in the wind from the Croaghs.
And that's as it should be –
except for the fact that, me,
at times I get tired and I like what I see
so much – a gap with a twenty-mile view to the sea –
I feel I could do with a rest for a while,
just something to lean on and stare –
and a gate, for example, would do.
That's all we think they are good for.

Francis Harvey

The Eviction

In early morning twilight, raw and chill,
Damp vapours brooding on the barren hill,
Through miles of mire in steady grave array
Threescore well-arm'd police pursue their way;
Each tall and bearded man a rifle swings,
And under each greatcoat a bayonet clings;
The Sheriff on his sturdy cob astride
Talks with the chief, who marches by their side,
And, creeping on behind them, Paudeen Dhu
Pretends his needful duty much to rue.
Six big-boned labourers, clad in common frieze,
Walk in the midst, the Sheriff's staunch allies;
Six crowbar men, from distant county brought, –
Orange, and glorying in their work, 'tis thought,
But wrongly, – churls of Catholics are they,
And merely hired at half a crown a day.

The hamlet clustering on its hill is seen,
A score of petty homesteads, dark and mean;
Poor always, not despairing until now;
Long used, as well as poverty knows how,
With life's oppressive trifles to contend.
This day will bring its history to an end.
Moveless and grim against the cottage walls
Lean a few silent men: but someone calls

Far off; and then a child 'without a stitch'
Runs out of doors, flies back with piercing screech,
And soon from house to house is heard the cry
Of female sorrow, swelling loud and high,
Which makes the men blaspheme between their teeth.
Meanwhile, o'er fence and watery field beneath,
The little army moves through drizzling rain;
A 'Crowbar' leads the Sheriff's nag; the lane
Is enter'd, and their plashing tramp draws near;
One instant, outcry holds its breath to hear;
'Halt!' – at the doors they form in double line,
And ranks of polish'd rifles wetly shine.

The Sheriff's painful duty must be done;
He begs for quiet – and the work's begun.
The strong stand ready; now appear the rest,
Girl, matron, grandsire, baby on the breast,
And Rosy's thin face on a pallet borne;
A motley concourse, feeble and forlorn.
One old man, tears upon his wrinkled cheek,
Stands trembling on a threshold, tries to speak,
But, in defect of any word for this,
Mutely upon the doorpost prints a kiss,
Then passes out for ever. Through the crowd
The children run bewilder'd, wailing loud;

Where needed most, the men combine their aid;
And, last of all, is Oona forth convey'd,
Reclined in her accustom'd strawen chair,
Her aged eyelids closed, her thick white hair
Escaping from her cap; she feels the chill,
Looks round and murmurs, then again is still.

Now bring the remnants of each household fire;
On the wet ground the hissing coals expire;
And Paudeen Dhu, with meekly dismal face,
Receives the full possession of the place . . .

William Allingham

The Snare

I hear a sudden cry of pain!
  There is a rabbit in a snare:
Now I hear the cry again,
  But I cannot tell from where.

But I cannot tell from where
  He is calling out for aid;
Crying on the frightened air,
  Making everything afraid,

Making everything afraid
  Wrinkling up his little face,
As he cries again for aid;
  And I cannot find the place!

And I cannot find the place
  Where his paw is in the snare;
Little one! Oh, little one!
  I am searching everywhere.

James Stephens

Memoirs of a Fallen Blackbird

They liked me when I was on the wing
And I could whistle and I could sing;
But now that I am in my bed of clay
They come no more to be with me.

It was on the main road halfway between
Newcastle West and Abbeyfeale;
A juggernaught glanced me as it passed me by
And that was the end of the road for me.

Later that day, as I lay on the verge,
A thin rake of a young man picked me up
Into his trembling hands, and he stared
At me full quarter of an hour, he stared

At me and then he laid me down
And with his hands scooped me a shallow grave;
His soul passed into me as he covered me o'er;
I fear for him now where'er he be.

They liked me when I was on the wing
And I could whistle and I could sing;
But now that I am in my bed of clay
They come no more to be with me.

Paul Durcan

Innocence

They laughed at one I loved –
The triangular hill that hung
Under the Big Forth. They said
That I was bounded by the whitethorn hedges
Of the little farm and did not know the world.
But I knew that love's doorway to life
Is the same doorway everywhere.

Ashamed of what I loved
I flung her from me and called her a ditch
Although she was smiling at me with violets.

But now I am back in her briary arms
The dew of an Indian Summer morning lies
On bleached potato-stalks –
What age am I?

I do not know what age I am,
I am no mortal age;
I know nothing of women,
Nothing of cities,
I cannot die
Unless I walk outside these whitethorn hedges.

Patrick Kavanagh

Seumas Beg

A man was sitting underneath a tree
Outside the village; and he asked me what
Name was upon this place; and said that he
Was never here before – He told a lot

Of stories to me too. His nose was flat!
I asked him how it happened, and he said
– The first mate of the *Mary Anne* did that
With a marling-spike one day – but he was dead.

And jolly good job too; and he'd have gone
A long way to have killed him – Oh, he had
A gold ring in one ear; the other
– 'Was bit off by a crocodile, bedad!'

That's what he said. He taught me how to chew!
He was a real nice man. He liked me too!

James Stephens

Beg-Innish

Bring Kateen-Beag and Maurya Jude
To dance in Beg-Innish,
And when the lads (they're in Dunquin)
Have sold their crabs and fish,
Wave fawney shawls and call them in,
And call the little girls who spin,
And seven weavers from Dunquin
To dance in Beg-Innish.

I'll play you jigs, and Maurice Kean,
Where nets are laid to dry,
I've silken strings would draw a dance
From girls are lame or shy;
Four strings I've brought from Spain and France
To make your long men skip and prance,
Till stars look out to see the dance
Where nets are laid to dry.

We'll have no priest or peeler in
To dance at Beg-Innish;
But we'll have drink from M'riarty Jim
Rowed round while gannets fish,
A keg with porter to the brim,
That every lad may have his whim,
Till we up with sails with M'riarty Jim
And sail from Beg-Innish.

John Millington Synge

Above

A lone grey heron is flying, flying
    Home to her nest,
And over the rush-blown waters
    Burning in the west,
Where an orange moon is lying
    Softly on soft air,
As the dusk comes lounging after
    Sleepy care.

Ah, now that heron is slowly, slowly
    Plying her wing,
But soon she'll droop to the rushes
    Where the winds swing;
She'll stand in the pools and coldly
    Dream on the sly,
With her wild eyes watching the fishes,
    As stars watch you from on high.

F. R. Higgins

An Old Woman of the Roads

Oh, to have a little house!
To own the hearth and stool and all!
The heaped up sods against the fire,
The pile of turf against the wall!

To have a clock with weights and chains
And pendulum swinging up and down!
A dresser filled with shining delph,
Speckled and white and blue and brown!

I could be busy all the day
Clearing and sweeping hearth and floor,
And fixing on their shelf again
My white and blue speckled store!

I could be quiet there at night
Beside the fire and by myself,
Sure of a bed and loath to leave
The ticking clock and the shining delph!

Och! but I'm weary of mist and dark,
And roads where there's never a house nor bush,
And tired I am of bog and road,
And the crying wind and the lonesome hush!

And I am praying to God on high,
And I am praying Him night and day,
For a little house – a house of my own –
Out of the wind's and the rain's way.

Padraic Colum

April Fool

Here come I, old April Fool,
Between March hare and nuts in May.
Fool me forward, fool me back,
Hares will dance and nuts will crack.

Here come I, my fingers crossed
Between the shuffle and the deal.
Fool me flush or fool me straight,
Queens are wild and queens will wait.

Here come I, my clogs worn out
Between the burden and the song.
Fool me hither, fool me hence,
Keep the sound but ditch the sense.

Here come I, my hair on fire,
Between the devil and the deep.
Fool me over, fool me down,
Sea shall dry and devil shall drown.

Here come I, in guts and brass,
Between the raven and the pit.
Fool me under, fool me flat,
Coffins land on Ararat.

Here come I, old April Fool,
Between the hoar frost and the fall.
Fool me drunk or fool me dry,
Spring comes back, and back come I.

Louis MacNeice

Allie

Allie, call the birds in,
    The birds from the sky!
Allie calls, Allie sings,
    Down they all fly:
First there came
Two white doves,
    Then a sparrow from his nest,
Then a clucking bantam hen,
    Then a robin red-breast.

Allie, call the beasts in,
    The beasts, every one!
Allie calls, Allie sings,
    In they all run:
First there came
Two black lambs,
    Then a grunting Berkshire sow,
Then a dog without a tail,
    Then a red and white cow.

Allie, call the fish up,
    The fish from the stream!
Allie calls, Allie sings,
    Up they all swim:
First there came
Two gold fish,
    A minnow and a miller's thumb,
Then a school of little trout,
    Then the twisting eels come.

Allie, call the children,
    Call them from the green!
Allie calls, Allie sings,
    Soon they run in:
First there came
Tom and Madge,
    Kate and I who'll not forget
How we played by the water's edge
    Till the April sun set.

Robert Graves

A Tune on a Reed

I have a pipe of oaten straw,
   I play upon it when I may,
And the music that I draw
   Is as happy as the day.

It has seven holes, and I
   Play upon it high and low;
I can make it laugh and cry,
   I can make it banish woe.

Any tune you like to name
   I will play it at the word,
Old or new is all the same,
   I'm as ready as a bird.

No one pipes so happily,
   Not a piper can succeed
When I lean against a tree
   Blowing gently on my reed.

James Stephens

The Rainmakers

for Esther

We shake the young birches
hung with fat raindrops:
local showers that drench
only you and me; witch
doctors, I know, do it
better but this is
personal rainmaking,
private weather. Listen
to the laughter of myself
and my daughter under
the dripping birches.

Francis Harvey

Down in the Alley-O

Down in the Alley-O
Where we play Relievi-O
Up comes her mother-O
Have you seen my Mary-O?
Why did you let her go?
Because she bit my finger-O!
Which finger did she bite?
The little finger on my right.

Traditional

Hey, Ho, Skippety Toe

Hey, ho, skippety toe
Turn the ship and around we go
Judy and Jack
Dressed in black
Silver buttons all down their back.

Traditional

Brian O Linn

Brian O Linn had no breeches to wear.
He got an old sheepskin to make him a pair
With the fleshy side out and the woolly side in,
'They'll be pleasant and cool,' says Brian O Linn.

Brian O Linn had no shirt to his back,
He went to a neighbour's and borrowed a sack,
Then he puckered the meal bag in under his chin –
'Sure they'll take them for ruffles,' says Brian O Linn.

Brian O Linn was hard up for a coat,
So he borrowed the skin of a neighbouring goat,
With the horns sticking out from his oxsters, and then,
'Sure they'll take them for pistols,' says Brian O Linn.

Brian O Linn had no hat to put on,
So he got an old beaver to make him a one,
There was none of the crown left and less of the brim,
'Sure there's fine ventilation,' says Brian O Linn.

Brian O Linn had no brogues for his toes,
He hopped in two crab-shells to serve him for those.
Then he split up two oysters that match'd like a twin,
'Sure they'll shine out like buckles,' says Brian O Linn.

Brian O Linn had no watch to put on,
So he scooped out a turnip to make him a one.
Then he placed a young cricket in under the skin –
'Sure they'll think it is ticking,' says Brian O Linn.

Brian O Linn to his house had no door,
He'd the sky for a roof, and the bog for a floor
He'd a way to jump out and a way to swim in,
''Tis a fine habitation,' says Brian O Linn.

Brian O Linn went a-courting one night,
He set both the mother and daughter to fight;
To fight for his hand they both stripped to the skin,
'Sure! I'll marry you both,' says Brian O Linn.

Brian O Linn, his wife and wife's mother,
They all lay down in the bed together,
The sheets they were old and the blankets were thin,
'Lie close to the wall,' says Brian O Linn.

Brian O Linn, his wife and wife's mother,
Were all going home o'er the bridge together,
The bridge it broke down, and they all tumbled in,
'We'll go home by the water,' says Brian O Linn.

Anon.

Finnegan's Wake

Tim Finnegan liv'd in Walkin Street
    A gentleman Irish mighty odd.
He had a tongue both rich and sweet,
    An' to rise in the world he carried a hod.
Now Tim had a sort of a tipplin' way
    With the love of the liquor he was born,
An' to help him on with his work each day,
    He'd a drop of the craythur ev'ry morn.

Chorus:
Whack folthedah, dance to your partner
Welt the flure yer trotters shake,
Wasn't it the truth I told you,
Lots of fun at Finnegan's Wake.

One morning Tim was rather full,
    His head felt heavy which made him shake,
He fell from the ladder and broke his skull,
    So they carried him home his corpse to wake.
They rolled him up in a nice clean sheet,
    And laid him out upon the bed,
With a gallon of whiskey at his feet,
    And a barrel of porter at his head.

His friends assembled at the wake,
    And Mrs Finnegan called for lunch,
First they brought in tay and cake,
    Then pipes, tobacco and whiskey punch.
Miss Biddy O'Brien began to cry,
    'Such a neat clean corpse, did you ever see,
Arrah, Tim avourneen, why did you die?'
    'Ah, hould your gab,' said Paddy McGee.

Then Biddy O'Connor took up the job,
    'Biddy,' says she, 'you're wrong, I'm sure,'
But Biddy gave her a belt in the gob,
    And left her sprawling on the floor;
Oh, then the war did so on enrage;
    'Twas woman to woman and man to man,
Shillelagh law did all engage,
    And a row and a ruction soon began.

Then Micky Maloney raised his head,
    When a noggin of whiskey flew at him,
It missed and falling on the bed,
    The liquor scattered over Tim;
Bedad he revives, see how he rises,
    And Timothy rising from the bed,
Says, 'Whirl your liquor round like blazes,
    Thanam o'n dhoul, do ye think I'm dead?'

Anon.

145

The Last Irish Snake

Far out to ocean St Patrick drove
The snakes from Ireland like a drove
Of shorthorns beyond the Great Blasket
Still clouding, unclouding, mountainous ridges.
He cursed them, tail and blastoderm
And with his crozier, rid
The rocky corners. Coil over coil
Big and small families of outcasts,
Heads still held high, were hurrying,
No time to lay their eggs or cast
A skin, for his Latin lightened, hurled
More bolts at them: chariot wheels
Rolling downhill from the hub
By bush and boulder as they scattered
With green stripes, yellow dots of charlock,
Land-snakes, water-snakes, all hubble-bubble,
Hundreds and hundreds of them scattered by
Jubilant hymn.
                              But one old serpent
Sternly refused to be so servile
And leave Lough Allen, his habitat,
Although it flapped at the holy habit
Of the saint with rage. He showed his fang,
Indignant at these new-fangled ways,

And called to Aesculapius
In vain for he was quickly ousted.
Slowly he scaled and wriggled, eskered
Himself along alluvial soil,
Muddied, a trail of slime. Unsoiled
The water followed with bright reflection
Of intertwining blacks, of golden flecks.
People ten miles away at Roosky
Could hear him unearthing and their roosters
Clapped wings and dropped. The portly monster
Burrowing southward, left Lough Ree.
Wild duck came down, but saw no reeds.
He stopped to untangle at Portumna
And hold a public demonstration.
Scraw, scrub, thorn-bushes, thistles, briars
Rock, stone, were tossing up and down
As though he were Briarius
Twitched by a hundred dowsing rods,
His only form of rodomontade.
He worked like a huge excavator
With bucketed back digging a cavern
To hide in. Sacred skin was torn
To strips. The water, a brown-white torrent,
Was soon Lough Derg: another lake that
His blood was colouring with lake.
Onward trundled the great Batrachian

By Foynes, Askeaton, Tarbet, Kilrush
Until the new River Shannon was rushing
South-westward, with small church, shanty,
And farm in flood. He passed Loop Head
And Kerry Head, loop after loop,
Then, left, between those far escarpments,
Day shining on an estuary,
And sank as if he were bedevilled,
Cabling along the ocean bed.

Austin Clarke

Welsh Incident

'But that was nothing to what things came out
From the sea-caves of Criccieth yonder.'
                    'What were they? Mermaids? dragons?
        ghosts?'
'Nothing at all of any things like that.'
'What were they, then?'
                              'All sorts of queer things,
Things never seen or heard or written about,
Very strange, un-Welsh, utterly peculiar
Things. Oh, solid enough they seemed to
        touch,
Had anyone dared it. Marvellous creation,
All various shapes and sizes and no sizes,
All new, each perfectly unlike his neighbour,
Though all came moving slowly out together.'
'Describe just one of them.'
                              'I am unable.'
'What were their colours?'
                              'Mostly nameless
        colours,
Colours you'd like to see; but one was puce
Or perhaps more like crimson, but not
                    purplish.
Some had no colour.'
                              'Tell me, had they legs?'

'Not a leg or foot among them that I saw.'
'But did these things come out in any order?
What o'clock was it? What was the day of the week?
Who else was present? How was the weather?'
'I was coming to that. It was half past three
On Easter Tuesday last. The sun was shining.
The Harlech Silver Band played *Marchog Jesu*
On thirty-seven shimmering instruments,
Collecting for Carnarvon's (Fever) Hospital Fund.
The populations of Pwllheli, Criccieth,
Portmadoc, Borth, Tremadoc, Penrhyndeudraeth,
Were all assembled. Criccieth's mayor addressed them
First in good Welsh and then in fluent English,
Twisting his fingers in his chain of office,
Welcoming the things. They came out on the sand,
Not keeping time to the band, moving sea-ward
Silently at a snail's pace. But at last
The most odd, indescribable thing of all
Which hardly one man there could see for wonder
Did something recognizably a something.'
'Well, what?'
                    'It made a noise.'
                              'A frightening
    noise?'
'No, no.'
        'A musical noise? A noise of scuffling?'

150

'No, but a very loud, respectable noise –
Like groaning to oneself on Sunday morning
In Chapel, close before the second psalm.'
'What did the mayor do?'
                              'I was coming to that.'

Robert Graves

Evidence

Along the wandering strand the sea unloads glass balls
Jellyfish, broken shells, its tangle
Of nets, cork, bits of wood,
Coral. A crooked line paid out on sand.
Here's evidence; gather it all up.

Time on window-panes
Imposes a curved edge of dust,
Hides dirt under the refrigerator, invites
The mice inside to dodge
Behind the revealing stack of empty bottles.
In the refrigerator the ice is growing
Into odd shapes; outside
The house, the cracks are spreading
In the asphalt; they reach out, join
To weave some kind of message.

Age creates
People whose wrinkles betray
How they smiled, with scars
Of operations. They have white patches
Where the sun has not reached them:
The skin grows hard on their hands;
Some of them have false teeth.
The flick of their lashes, the flutter of their shirtfronts
Is evidence of life.

Eiléan Ní Chuilleanáin

Celibates

When farmers burned the furze away
Where they had heedlessly lived till then
The hermits all made for the sea-shore,
Chose each a far safe hole beneath rocks,
Now more alone than even before.

Nights darker than thickest hawthorn-shade;
The March wind blew in cold off the sea.
They never again saw a sunrise
But watched the long sands glitter westwards.
Their bells cracked, their singing grew harsher.

In August a bee, strayed overboard
Down the high cliff, hummed along the strand.
Three hermits saw him on that long coast.
One spring the high tides stifled them all.

Eileán Ní Chuilleanáin

Margadh Na Gruaige

An raibh tú riamh ag margadh na gruaige?
Tá sé thíos ar dheis láimh le margadh na n-éan.
Caitheann tú triall go mall tré ghréasán de
    shráideanna cúnga
i mbaile beag Francach a bhaineann leis an
    Mheánaois.

Tá gleo is clampar ann is hurlamaboc.
Ceantálaithe ag glaoch amach os ard,
an praghas is airde á fhógairt acu go rábach,
iad ag díol is ag ceannach, ag cantáil ar gach slám.

Is chífidh tú trilseáin dualach' dualánach'
ag sníomh go talamh ann ina slaodaibh mín nó borb.
Cúilí réamhrá dho á n-ionramháil le racaí;
giollaí á cíoradh, bánlaimh I ndiaidh banláimhe.

An raibh tú riamh ag margadh na gruaige?
Do chuas-sa ann liom fhéin aon uair amháin.
Do gearradh díom m'fholt rua ó bhonn na cluaise
is díoladh ar phraghas ard é la sabhdán.

Nuala Ní Dhomhnaill

The Hair Market

Did you ever go to the Hair Market?
It's down on the right-hand side of the Bird Market.
You have to thread slowly through narrow streets
In a little medieval town in France.

It's there you'll hear the noise and fuss and uproar,
The auctioneers shouting over their megaphones,
Screaming the highest bid at the top of their voices,
Buying and selling, cutting deals at every turn.

And it's there you'll see plaits and chignons and
    ponytails
Flowing smooth or curling from ceiling to floor,
Heaps of tresses raked and teased out,
Servants combing them, armslength after armslength.

Were you ever in the Hair Market?
I went there once myself on a certain day.
They cut my long red locks close to my skull,
And sold them to a Sultan for the best price of all.

Nuala Ní Dhomhnaill
Translated by Eiléan Ní Chuilleanáin

Monkeys

Two little creatures
With faces the size of
A pair of pennies
Are clasping each other.
'Ah, do not leave me,'
One says to the other,
In the high monkey-
Cage in the beast-shop.

There are no people
To gape at them now,
For people are loth to
Peer in the dimness;
Have they not builded
Streets and playhouses.
Sky-signs and bars,
To lose the loneliness
Shaking the hearts
Of the two little Monkeys?

Yes. But who watches
The penny-small faces
Can hear the voices:
'Ah, do not leave me;
Suck I will give you,
Warmth and clasping,
And if you slip from
This beam I can never
Find you again.'

Dim is the evening,
And chill is the weather;
There, drawn from their coloured
Hemisphere,
The apes lilliputian
With faces the size of
A pair of pennies,
And voices as low as
The flow of my blood.

Padraic Colum

Arches

Arches on land,
half-circles only,
might dream
of what they miss.

And yet to stand
in a dark stream,
is this
not twice as lonely?

Richard Kell

from 'The Inchichore Haiku'

On a brick chimney
I can see all West Limerick
in a jackdaw's eye.

Michael Hartnett

The Faery Earl

Oh, who is this comes ridin',
    Ridin' down the glen?
Is it one of our own Red-Branch Knights
    Or one of the King's men?

With feathers on his helmet,
    And gold upon his shield,
His horse is shod with silver shoes,
    He ridin' through the field!

Oh, this is not a Red-Branch
    Nor one of the King's men,
But this is faery Desmond
    Come ridin' back again.

'O lady of the Castle,
    O lady with gold hair,
O lady with eyes of pity,
    Come down the grey tower stair.

'For I may ask a question,
    And you may answer me,
When the sun is red in the forest,
    And the moon is white on the sea.'

Says she, 'Sir, ask your question,
    And I will answer you;
At sunset or at moonrise
    God send that I speak true!

'I know you by your helmet,
    And by your voice so sweet,
And by your coal-black charger
    With silver on his feet.

'God send you, faery Desmond,
    To come back to your own.'
Says he, 'Your answer, lady,
    Before the sun goes down.

'I'm ridin' ever and ever
    Over the land and sea;
My horse's shoes of silver,
    How long will they last me?'

The lady stood and pondered,
  The salt tear in her eye –
'Oh, would that I had magic
    To make a wise reply.

'Oh, will they wear forever,
    Or will they wear out fast?
Will he ride home this even'
    And stable his horse at last?'

'Sweet lady, quick, your answer!'
    'Now, God, what can I say? –
Those silver shoes will last, sir,
    To ride till Judgement Day.'

He turned, that faery horseman,
    And shook his bridle rein;
'Now, come the Day of Judgement
    Ere I ride home again.'

The sun went down in the forest,
    The moon shone bright as pearl,
The lady lay in the castle,
    And died for the faery Earl.

And ye will see him ridin',
    Ridin' down the glen
Over the seas and the rivers,
    Over the hill and the plain.

Ye'll see the plume on his helmet
    Waftin' among the trees,
And the silver shoes of his charger
    Chasin' the moonlit seas.

He's ridin' ever and ever,
   He'll ride till Judgement Day;
Oh, when that ride is over,
   May he ride home, we pray!

Rosa Mulholland

Mise Raifteirí

Mise Raifteirí, an file, lán dóchais is grá
le súile gan solas, ciúineas gan crá,
ag dul síos ar m'aistear le solas mo chroí,
fann agus tuirseach go deireadh mo shlí;
tá mé anois lem aghaidh ar Bhalla
ag seinm cheoil do phócaí falamh'.

Anton Raifteirí

I Am Raftery the Poet

I am Raftery the poet.
Full of hope and love,
My eyes without sight,
My mind without torment.

Going west on my journey
By the light of my heart,
Tired and weary
To the end of the road.

Behold me now
With my back to the wall.
Playing music
To empty pockets.

Anthony Raftery
Translated by James Stephens

Lament for Owen Roe O'Neill

'Did they dare, did they dare, to slay Owen
  Roe O'Neill!'
"Yes, they slew with poison him they feared to meet
  with steel."
'May God wither up their hearts! May their
  blood cease to flow!
May they walk in living death, who poisoned
  Owen Roe!

Though it break my heart to hear, say again
  the bitter words.'
"From Derry, against Cromwell, he marched to
  measure swords;
But the weapon of the Saxon met him on his way,
And he died at Clough-Oughter, upon St
  Leonard's Day."

'Wail, wail ye for The Mighty One! Wail, wail ye for
  the Dead;
Quench the hearth, and hold the breath – with ashes
  strew the head.
How tenderly we loved him! How deeply we deplore!
Holy Saviour! but to think we shall never see him
  more.

Sagest in the council was he, – kindest in the hall,
Sure we never won a battle – 'twas Owen won them all.
Had he lived – had he lived – our dear country had
  been free;
But he's dead, but he's dead, and 'tis slaves we'll ever be.

O'Farrell and Clanrickard, Preston and Red Hugh,
Audley and MacMahon – ye are valiant, wise and true;
But – what, what are ye all to our darling who is gone?
The Rudder of our Ship was he, our Castle's corner
    stone!

Wail, wail him through the Island! Weep, weep for our
    pride!
Would that on the battle-field our gallant chief had
    died!
Weep the Victor of Benburb – weep him, young man
    and old;
Weep for him, ye women – your Beautiful lies cold!

We thought you would not die – we were sure you
    would not go,
And leave us in our utmost need to Cromwell's cruel
    blow –
Sheep without a shepherd, when the snow shuts out
    the sky –
O! why did you leave us, Owen? Why did you die?

Soft as woman's was your voice, O'Neill! bright was
    your eye.
O! why did you leave us, Owen? Why did you die?
Your troubles are all over, you're at rest with God on
    high;
But we're slaves, and we're orphans, Owen! – why did
    you die!'

Thomas Davis

Requiem for the Croppies

The pockets of our great coats full of barley –
No kitchens on the run, no striking camp –
We moved quick and sudden in our own country.
The priest lay behind ditches with the tramp.
A people, hardly marching – on the hike –
We found new tactics happening each day:
We'd cut through reins and rider with the pike
And stampede cattle into infantry,
Then retreat through hedges where cavalry must be
    thrown.
Until, on Vinegar Hill, the fatal conclave.
Terraced thousands died, shaking scythes at cannon.
The hillside blushed, soaked in our broken wave.
They buried us without shroud or coffin
And in August the barley grew up out of the grave.

Seamus Heaney

The Rivals

I heard a bird at dawn
    Singing sweetly on a tree,
That the dew was on the lawn
    And the wind was on the lea;
But I didn't listen to him,
    For he didn't sing to me.

I didn't listen to him,
    For he didn't sing to me
That the dew was on the lawn
    And the wind was on the lea;
I was singing at the time
    Just as prettily as he.

I was singing all the time,
    Just as prettily as he,
About the dew upon the lawn
    And the wind upon the lea;
So I didn't listen to him
    As he sang upon a tree.

James Stephens

John-John

I dreamt last night of you, John-John,
    And thought you called to me;
And when I woke this morning, John,
    Yourself I hoped to see;
But I was all alone, John-John,
    Though still I heard your call:
I put my boots and bonnet on,
    And took my Sunday shawl,
And went, full sure to find you, John,
        To Nenagh fair.

The fair was just the same as then,
    Five years ago to-day,
When first you left the thimble men
    And came with me away;
For there again were thimble men
    And shooting galleries,
And card-trick men and Maggie men
    Of all sorts and degrees –
But not a sight of you, John-John,
        Was anywhere.

I turned my face to home again,
    And called myself a fool
To think you'd leave the thimble men
    And live again by rule,
And go to mass and keep the fast
    And till the little patch:
My wish to have you home was past
    Before I raised the latch
And pushed the door and saw you, John,
                Sitting down there.

How cool you came in here, begad
    As if you owned the place!
But rest yourself there now, my lad,
    'Tis good to see your face;
My dream is out, and now by it
    I think I know my mind:
At six o'clock this house you'll quit,
    And leave no grief behind; –
But until six o'clock, John-John,
                My bit you'll share.

My neighbours' shame of me began
  When first I brought you in;
To wed and keep a tinker man
  They thought a kind of sin;
But now this three year since you're gone
  'Tis pity me they do,
And that I'd rather have, John-John,
  Than that they'd pity you.
Pity for me and you, John-John,
          I could not bear.

Oh, you're my husband right enough,
  But what's the good of that?
You know you never were the stuff
  To be the cottage cat,
To watch the fire and hear me lock
  The door and put out Shep –
But there now, it is six o'clock
  And time for you to step.
God bless and keep you far, John-John!
          And that's my prayer.

                              Thomas MacDonagh

She Moved through the Fair

My young love said to me, 'My brothers won't mind,
And my parents won't slight you for your lack of kind.'
Then she stepped away from me, and this she did say,
'It will not be long, love, till our wedding day.'

She stepped away from me and she moved through
    the fair,
And fondly I watched her go here and go there.
Then she went her way homeward with one star
    awake,
As the swan in the evening moves over the lake.

The people were saying no two were e'er wed
But one had a sorrow that never was said,
And I smiled as she passed with her goods and her
    gear,
And that was the last that I saw of my dear.

I dreamt it last night that my young love came in.
So softly she entered, her feet made no din;
She came close beside me, and this she did say,
'It will not be long, love, till our wedding day.'

Padraic Colum

Moonrise

I awoke in the Midsummer not-to-call night, in the
    white and the walk of the morning:
The moon, dwindled and thinned to the fringe of a
    fingernail held to the candle,
Or paring of paradisaïcal fruit, lovely in waning but
    lustreless,
Stepped from the stool, drew back from the barrow,
    of dark Maenefa the mountain;
A cusp still clasped him, a fluke yet fanged him,
    entangled him, not quit utterly.
This was the prized, the desirable sight, unsought,
    presented so easily,
Parted me leaf and leaf, divided me, eyelid and
    eyelid of slumber.

Gerard Manley Hopkins

Lightning

At a decent distance
From the heads of men
I happen

And am gone.
This is how
I light up heaven

And define the dark.
You think I must
Be something of an exhibitionist,

A dramatic braggart of light?
I am a mere moment
Between this and that

Yet so much that moment
I
Illumine the sky

And the small homes of men,
Flash through their fears, spotlight their joys.
My deepest nature is quiet and private.
I cannot escape the noise.

Brendan Kennelly

Flying Crooked

The butterfly, a cabbage white,
(His honest idiocy of flight)
Will never now, it is too late,
Master the art of flying straight,
Yet has – who knows so well as I? –
A just sense of how not to fly:
He lurches here and here by guess
And God and hope and hopelessness.
Even the aerobatic swift
Has not his flying-crooked gift.

Robert Graves

Lollocks

By sloth on sorrow fathered,
These dusty-featured Lollocks
Have their nativity in all disordered
Backs of cupboard drawers.

They play hide and seek
Among collars and novels
And empty medicine bottles,
And letters from abroad
That never will be answered.

Every sultry night
They plague little children,
Gurgling from the cistern,
Humming from the air,
Skewing up the bed-clothes
Twitching the blind.

When the imbecile aged
Are over-long in dying
And the nurse drowses,
Lollocks come skipping
Up the tattered stairs
And are nasty together
In the bed's shadow.

The signs of their presence
Are boils on the neck,
Dreams of vexation suddenly recalled
In the middle of the morning,
Languor after food.

Men cannot see them,
Men cannot hear them,
Do not believe in them –
But suffer the more,
Both in neck and belly.

Women can see them –
Oh those naughty wives
Who sit by the fireside
Munching bread and honey,
Watching them in mischief
From corners of their eyes,
Slily allowing them to lick
Honey-sticky fingers.

Sovereign against Lollocks
Are hard broom and soft broom,
To well comb the hair,
To well brush the shoe,
And to pay every debt
So soon as it's due.

Robert Graves

Sweeney Praises the Trees

The branchy leafy oak-tree
is highest in the wood,
the shooting hazel bushes
hide sweet hazel-nuts.

The alder is my darling
all thornless in the gap,
some milk of human kindness
coursing in its sap.

The blackthorn is a jaggy creel,
stippled with dark sloes;
green watercress is thatch on wells
where the drinking blackbird goes.

Sweetest of the leafy stalks,
the vetches strew the pathway;
the oyster-grass is my delight
and the wild strawberry.

Low-set clumps of apple-trees
drum down fruit when shaken;
scarlet berries clot like blood
on mountain rowan.

Briars curl in sideways,
arch a stickle back,
draw blood, and curl back innocent
to sneak the next attack.

The yew-tree in each churchyard
wraps night in its dark hood;
ivy is a shadowy
genius of the wood.

Holly rears its windbreak,
a door in winter's face;
Life-blood on a spear-shaft
darkens the grain of ash.

Birch-tree, smooth and pale-skinned,
delicious to the breeze,
high twigs plait and crown it
the queen of trees.

The aspen pales
and whispers, hesitates:
a thousand frightened scuts
race in its leaves.

But what disturbs me most
in the living wood
is the swishing to and fro
of an oak-rod.

Anon.
Translated by Seamus Heaney

Thatcher

Bespoke for weeks, he turned up some morning
Unexpectedly, his bicycle slung
With a light ladder and a bag of knives.
He eyed the old rigging, poked at the eaves,

Opened and handled sheaves of lashed wheat-straw.
Next, the bundled rods: hazel and willow
Were flicked for weight, twisted in case they'd snap.
It seemed he spent the morning warming up:

Then fixed the ladder, laid out well honed blades
And snipped at straw and sharpened ends of rods
That, bent in two, made a white-pronged staple
For pinning down his world, handful by handful.

Couchant for days on sods above the rafters
He shaved and flushed the butts, stitched all together
Into a sloped honeycomb, a stubble patch,
And left them gaping at his Midas touch.

Seamus Heaney

Fishing Harbour towards Evening

Slashed clouds leak gold. Along the slurping wharf
The snugged boats creak and seesaw. Round the masts

Abrasive squalls flake seagulls off the sky:
Choppy with wings the rapids of shrill sound.

Wrapt in sliced airs of fish and tar,
Light wincing on their knives, the clockwork men

Incise and scoop the oily pouches, flip
The soft guts overboard with blood-wet fingers.

Among three rhythms the slapping silver turns
To polished icy marble upon the deck.

Richard Kell

The Painting

Under the rose-tree's dancing shade
   There stands a little ivory girl,
   Pulling the leaves of pink and pearl
With pale green nails of polished jade.

The red leaves fall upon the mould,
   The white leaves flutter, one by one,
   Down to a blue bowl where the sun,
Like a great dragon, writhes in gold.

The white leaves float upon the air,
   The red leaves flutter idly down,
   Some fall upon her yellow gown,
And some upon her raven hair.

She takes an amber lute and sings,
   And as she sings a silver crane
   Begins his scarlet neck to strain,
And flap his burnished metal wings.

With pale green nails of polished jade,
    Pulling the leaves of pink and pearl,
    There stands a little ivory girl
Under the rose tree's dancing shade.

Oscar Wilde

Under the Stairs

Look in the dark alcove under the stairs:
a paintbrush steeped in turpentine, its hairs

softening for use; rat-poison in a jar;
bent spoons for prising lids; a spare fire-bar;

the shaft of a broom; a tyre; assorted nails;
a store of candles for when the light fails.

Frank Ormsby

Nearer Home

My father is standing outside the front door,
pointing out to me the Plough and North Star.
He says, 'Look up, child, just as far as you can.'
I see freckles join up on the back of his hand.

Vona Groarke

Boy Bathing

On the edge of the springboard
A boy poses, columned light
Poised.
Seagull's crying wrinkles
The brown parchment cliffs.
His body shines: a knife!
Spread wings, he opens
Plunges
Through the gold glass of sunshine
Smashes
In crumbs of glass the silence.

Denis Devlin

The Little Girl

The scratchy couch at my grandmother's
creaked as she pointed to a little girl
in a class photograph.
'And who's this?'
I brought the album
close to my face to decide.
All my brain would tell me was
'It's you, of course,
don't you even know yourself
when you see yourself?'
'It's me' I said,
although I couldn't remember
any of the girls or the dress.
'Look again' she said.

Julie O'Callaghan

White Sound

When rain
whispers
it is snow.

Julie O'Callaghan

from 'The Inchichore Haiku'

I push in a plug.
Mozart comes into the room
riding a cello.

Michael Hartnett

Telifís

faoi m'iníon Saffron

Ar a cúig a chlog ar maidin
Theastaigh an teilifís uaithi.
An féidir argóint le beainín
Dhá bhliain go leith?
Síos linn le chéile
Níor bhacas fiú le gléasadh
Is bhí an seomra préachta.
Gan solas fós sa spéir
Stánamar le hiontas ar scáileán bán.
Anois! Sásta?
Ach chonaic sise sneachta
Is sioráf tríd an sneachta
Is ulchabhán Artach
Ag faoleáil
Os a chionn.

Gabriel Rosenstock

Television

for my daughter Saffron

At five o'clock in the morning
She wanted television.
Who can argue with a little woman
Two and a half years old?
Down we went together
I didn't even dress
And the room was freezing.
No light yet in the sky
We stared in wonder at the white screen.
Happy now?
But she saw snow
And a giraffe through it
And an arctic owl
Wheeling
Above it.

Gabriel Rosenstock
Translated by Gabriel Fitzmaurice

Down by the Salley Gardens

Down by the salley gardens my love and I did
      meet;
She passed the salley gardens with little
      snow-white feet.
She bid me take love easy, as the leaves grow
      on the tree;
But I, being young and foolish, with her
      would not agree.

In a field by the river my love and I did stand,
And on my leaning shoulder she laid her
      snow-white hand.
She bid me take life easy, as the grass grows
      on the weirs;
But I was young and foolish, and now am full
      of tears.

W. B. Yeats

The Collarbone of a Hare

Would I could cast a sail on the water
Where many a king has gone
And many a king's daughter,
And alight at the comely trees and the lawn,
The playing upon pipes and the dancing,
And learn that the best thing is
To change my loves while dancing
And pay but a kiss for a kiss.

I would find by the edge of that water
The collarbone of a hare
Worn thin by the lapping of water,
And pierce it through with a gimlet, and stare
At the old bitter world where they marry in churches,
And laugh over the untroubled water
At all who marry in churches,
Through the white thin bone of a hare.

W. B. Yeats

Had I a Golden Pound

after the Irish

Had I a golden pound to spend,
My love should mend and sew no more.
And I would buy her a little quern,
Easy to turn on the kitchen floor.

And for her windows curtains white,
With birds in flight and flowers in bloom,
To face with pride the road to town,
And mellow down her sunlit room.

And with the silver change we'd prove
The truth of Love to life's own end,
With hearts the years could but embolden,
Had I a golden pound to spend.

Francis Ledwidge

Glossary

Buachaillín Ban / Bawn: White-headed boy, or fair-haired boy.

Cáhal Mór of the Wine-red Hand: One of the great O'Conors who was inaugurated as King of Connaught in 1201 and reigned for twenty-three years.

The Croppy Boy / Croppies: Untrained force, armed only with pikes, hayforks and a few guns, that took on the heavily armed British in the 1798 rebellion and were routed at Vinegar Hill. They got their name from cutting their hair short in sympathy with the French revolution.

Joseph Mary Plunkett and Thomas McDonagh: Among those executed in Dublin after the Easter Rising of 1916. On Easter Monday, 24 April 1916, the proclamation of the Provisional Government of the Irish Republic to the People of Ireland was read out from the steps of Dublin's GPO. Two of the signatories of that proclamation were Thomas Mac Donagh and Joseph Mary Plunkett, and they were among those to face the firing squad in Kilmainham jail after the rebels surrendered.

Owen Roe O'Neill: Irish military commander with experience of foreign wars who won a famous battle at Benburb in 1646. The story that he was poisoned is disputed.

Rath: Fort.

Tir na nOg: The literal translation is 'Land of the Young' and is used to refer to the afterlife – an Irish version of Valhalla.

Index of First Lines

Index of Poets

Acknowledgements

The author and the publisher would like to thank the following for their kind permission to reprint copyright material in this book:

Clarke, Austin: 'The Last Irish Snake' and 'A Strong Wind' from the *Wolfhound Book of Irish Poems for Young People* (1987), by permission of Merlin Press; **Colum, Padraic**: 'A Drover' from *Between Innocence and Peace* (1993), by permission of Mercier Press, 'An Old Woman of the Roads' from *Collected Poems* (1980), by permission of David Higham Ltd, 'A Cradle Song' by permission of New Island Books, 'She Moved Through the Fair' from *The School Bag* (1997 edition), by permission of Faber & Faber, 'Monkeys' from *Choice: Contemporary Irish Poetry Chosen by the Poets* (1977), by permission of Goldsmith Press; **Devlin, Denis**: 'Boy Bathing' by permission of Gallery Press; **Durcan, Paul**: 'Memoirs of a Fallen Blackbird' by permission of Harvill Press; **Fallon, Padraig**: 'Buachaillon Ban' by permission of Carcanet Press; **Graves, Robert**: 'Allie', 'Welsh Incident' from *Complete Poems Volume 2* (1997), by permission of Carcanet Press; **Groarke, Vona**: 'Nearer Home' from *Other People's Houses* (1999), by permission of Gallery Press; **Hartnett, Michael**: 'Lament for Tadhg Cronin's Children', 'I Saw Magic on a Green Country Road', 'The Inchichore Haiku' by permission of Gallery Press; **Harvey, Francis**: 'Gates', 'The Rainmakers' by permission of Dedalus Press; **Heaney, Seamus:** 'The Railway Children', 'Requiem for the Croppies', 'Thatcher' all reproduced by permission of Faber & Faber Ltd; **Kavanagh, Patrick**: 'Tarry Flynn', 'A Christmas Childhood', 'In Memory of my Mother', 'Innocence' all reproduced by permission of Jonathan Williams Literary Agency; **Kell, Richard**: 'Arches' from *Choice: Contemporary Irish Poetry Chosen by the Poets* (1977), by permission of Goldsmith Press; **Kennelly, Brendan**: 'Poem from a Three-year-old' by permission of Gallery Press; **Longley, Michael**: 'Halloween' from *Poems 1963–1983* (1991), by permission of Secker & Warburg, an imprint of Random House; **McDonagh, Donagh**: 'The Day Set for our Wedding' by permission of the Irish Humanities Centre; **MacNeice, Louis**: 'April Fool' from *Collected Poems* (1966), by permission of David Higham Ltd; **Ní Chuilleanáin, Eiléan**: 'Evidence', 'Celibates' by permission of Gallery Press; **Ní Dhomhnaill, Nuala**: 'The Hair Market' by permission of Gallery Press; **O'Callaghan, Julie**: 'Pumpkinhead' from *Two Barks*, 1998, 'White Sound' from *No Can Do*, 2000 by permission of Bloodaxe Books; **O'Riordain, Sean**: 'Cul an Ti' from *Poets of Munster*, ed. Sean Dunne (1985), by permission of Sairseal O Marcaigh; **O'Sullivan, Seumas**: 'A Piper' from *Between Innocence and Peace* (1993), by permission of Mercier Press; **Ormsby, Frank**: 'Under the Stairs' by permission of Gallery Press; **Rosenstock, Gabriel**: 'Telefis' and translation 'Television' by Gabriel Fitzmaurice from *Irish Poetry Now*, ed.Gabriel Fitzmaurice (1993), by permission of Merlin Press; **Simmons, James**: 'Claudy' by permission of Gallery Press; **Yeats, W. B.**: 'The Stolen Child', 'The Ballad of Father Gilligan', 'The Song of Wandering Aengus', 'The Fiddler of Dooney', 'The Cat and the Moon', 'Down by the Salley Gardens', 'The Collarbone of a Hare' all reproduced by permission of A. P. Watt Ltd.

Every effort has been made to trace the copyright holders, but if any have been inadvertently overlooked, the publisher will be pleased to make the necessary arrangement at the first opportunity.